PHOTOCOPIABLE

Learning in the Early Years

ACTIVITIES

Photocopiable activities for

Creative Development

Pauline Kenyon

Author
Pauline Kenyon

Editor
Jane Bishop

Assistant editor
Susan Howard

Series designer
Joy White

Designer
Heather C Sanneh

Illustrations
Clare Boyce

Cover photo
Garry Clarke

Published by Scholastic Ltd, Villiers House, Clarendon Avenue,
Leamington Spa, Warwickshire CV32 5PR

© 1998 Scholastic Ltd   Text © 1999 Pauline Kenyon
1 2 3 4 5 6 7 8 9 0   9 0 1 2 3 4 5 6 7 8

British Library Cataloguing-in-Publication Data
A catalogue record for this book is available from the British Library.

ISBN 0-590-53883-7

Contents

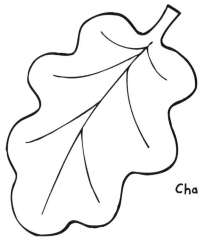

Introduction

This book is designed to help early years practitioners working in a wide range of settings, including those working in school nursery and reception classes, playgroups, voluntary groups and private and independent provision. It contains a large selection of photocopiable activities which focus on all the requirements of the *Desirable Outcomes for Children's Learning* in the area of Creative Development. It aims to provide a choice of useful materials which will be of benefit to very busy practitioners, saving them time in planning and preparation, leaving them more energy to engage with the children!

These requirements were originally published by the School Curriculum and Assessment Authority (SCAA) but are endorsed by the replacement body, the Qualifications and Curriculum Authority (QCA). As a condition for registration and funding in an LEA Early Years' Development Plan, settings must agree to promote the full range of 'Desirable Outcomes'. They will be inspected to give a judgement about the extent to which the quality of provision promotes the desirable outcomes in each of the six areas of learning. These areas are: Personal and Social Development, Language and Literacy, Mathematics, Knowledge and Understanding of the World, Physical Development and Creative Development.

The 'Desirable Outcomes' for learning in the area of Creative Development focus on the development of children's imagination and their ability to communicate and express ideas and feelings in creative ways.

'Children explore sound and colour, texture, shape, form and space in two and three dimensions. They respond in a variety of ways to what they see, hear, smell, touch and feel. Through art, music, dance, stories and imaginative play, they show an increasing ability to use their imagination, to listen and to observe. They use a widening range of materials, suitable tools, instruments and other resources to express ideas and to communicate their feelings.' (SCAA)

This book is a supplement to the *Learning in the Early Years – Creative Development* publication and covers the elements of the Desirable Outcomes for the Creative Development of children under five. It offers photocopiable materials which cover music, art, craft, drama and dance and imaginative play.

Each of the six areas of learning are covered by books in the original series and in their respective photocopiable activities supplementary publications.

The photocopiable activities

The activities in this book have been chosen to encourage children to use many different materials, tools and instruments and engage in a broad range of learning experiences across the curriculum. Most of the activities will usefully extend children's work in language and literacy and many will also support learning in numeracy and

personal and social development as well as other areas of learning. Almost all of the activities will provide valuable display material.

Most of the activities described in this book require the children to work in small groups, unless group size is otherwise specified. The activities have been designed to offer a range of enjoyable and purposeful tasks which are wider than simply 'pencil and paper' work which is swiftly completed. The sheets provide starting points which can then be developed both during the lesson and over the course of time. For instance, some of the drama activities develop the idea of making puppets which can then be later used in simple plays and presentations. Imaginative play activities first involve children in making and preparing materials which they then use to enhance their learning in the imaginative play area.

Assessment and record-keeping

Because the activities cover the full area of creative development, it will also be possible to use them for assessment purposes. Records could be built up by including a photocopied sheet of the original activity in each child's folder, to which you can add the date and brief notes with comments about any significant progress. These can then be used to plan further work. For example, a child with poor fine motor control who has difficulty using scissors might have a comment on one sheet that more practice is needed. Further work on cutting could be planned for him or her, with examples of this added to the file. If appropriate, examples or photographs of children's finished work could be included.

How to use this book

The book is designed so you can either follow a chapter through, using all the activities, or dip into it as you please. Although the activities are free-standing, a few of them, such as the 'Shoe box theatre' tasks in the drama section, can be used as a small topic over time.

When planning your creative development activities, do try to ensure that young children have regular experiences in music, art, craft, drama, dance and imaginative play. Avoid long gaps between activities in these areas. Under fives need a 'drip feed' approach to all these essential experiences to help them practise and consolidate their creative skills. This book is designed to help you cover a broad range of interesting and enjoyable tasks to give a secure foundation for their creative development.

All the activities require only everyday, readily available resources; many are designed to use recyclable materials. A good number of the activities will actually provide materials for further work, such as imaginative play 'props'.

The sheets can also be photocopied for parents to use at home with their children, providing valuable resources to develop home/school partnerships in education.

chapter one

Music

Develop the children's musical confidence with this range of creative ideas. Use simple percussion instruments to introduce high and low notes, play music patterns, learn about syllables and even compose individual tunes for the group to play back.

Sound flags

PAGE 9

Learning objective
To heighten listening skills.

What to do
Working with a small group of children, glue copies of the sheet onto card to provide one for each child. Talk together about the different instruments on the sheet and the sounds they make. Demonstrate with real instruments. Point to the printed names on the sheet and encourage the children to 'read' them with you, looking particularly at the first letter sound.

Let the children colour in each instrument then cut out the sections. Help them to fasten each one to a short stick, so that everyone has a set of six. Play the instruments and ask the children to hold up the matching flags, working as a group and then as individuals. Let them take turns holding up flags for the others to choose and play correct instruments.

Stairways

PAGE 10

Learning objective
To recognize high and low sounds.

What to do
Stick or photocopy the sheet onto thin card. Ask the children to colour in each step in the correct colour. Play a xylophone or glockenspiel and talk about different high and low notes showing the children the different sized bars. Explain that the notes are like going up and down a staircase. Let them watch and listen as you play ascending and descending notes, and ask them to point to the stairs on their sheets to show how the notes go higher or lower. Play individual notes and ask the children to point to the top (high notes) or bottom (low notes). Encourage them to point to coloured steps for you to play high or low. Then let the children take turns to play as you point to different colours.

Musical maps

PAGE 11

Learning objective
To learn to play different instruments and compose simple tunes.

What to do
Have a selection of drums, bells, triangles, cymbals and xylophones handy and demonstrate how to play each instrument correctly, letting the children take turns. Talk about tunes and how the children could compose their own.

Give each child a sheet and talk about the pictures of the instruments shown. Let them cut out the instrument squares and place them in the spaces provided to each make up their own tune. Talk about the patterns they have chosen and then let them stick the squares in place. Make up one of your own and demonstrate how your tune sounds. Give out the instruments and take turns to play each child's music, following their musical maps while you point to the correct place. Choose a title for each tune. Tape them to play to the whole class later.

PAGE 12

Notation grids
Learning objective
To make informal notation of music.
What to do
Collect together drums, triangles, cymbals, bells and shakers. Let the children play the instruments and discover the different sounds they make. Tell them that they are going to compose their own music. Divide a small group of children into pairs, give each pair a sheet and talk about the instruments in the pictures. Explain that they can decide how many beats or shakes they want for each instrument. Ask them to make a sign – one for each beat – to show this on the chart and to fill in their charts.

Give out the instruments. Hold each composition up in turn and conduct the children as they play, starting with the top line. Stick the sheets in an 'Our own music' book and put the book in a music area for children to play.

Louder, softer
PAGE 13
Learning objective
To discriminate between loud and softer sounds.
What to do
Photocopy or stick the sheet onto card. Ask the children to colour the loud card picture in red and the soft pictures in blue. Cut the pictures out. Explain that the red card has signs for loud and the blue card has signs for soft – both the word and picture tell us this. Say that instruments can make loud and soft sounds depending on how they are played. Play an instrument loudly and ask the children to listen carefully and then to hold up the relevant card. Check whether they are right and talk about the reasons. Play the same instrument softly. Check the cards the children hold up. Next, play different instruments in different ways and repeat the activity. Encourage the children to take turns to play the instruments, letting them show you which card they are playing and ask the others to guess.

Let the children draw in things that make loud and soft sounds in the spaces on the 'loud' and 'soft' cards.

Picture beats
PAGE 14
Learning objective
To match beats (syllables) to everyday objects.
What to do
Talk about beats – or syllables – in names. Demonstrate how to clap a name: John (one beat), Tedd-y (two), Miss-us-Wil-son (four), Sur-in-der (three). Encourage the group to clap their names, individually and then with everybody together.

Photocopy or stick the sheets onto card to provide one sheet for each child. Let them colour in and cut out the squares and arrange them in a pile facing downwards. Ask each child in turn to turn over the top card and show the group. Everybody says the name and claps the beats together. Go round the group until all the cards have been clapped. Extend the activity by letting individuals clap out the beats for each picture. Let them keep the card if they are correct. For the next round, each child shows two cards and this time each child must clap the two words.

8

Sound flags

Use these pictures to make flags.

Glue the sheet onto card, cut out the cards and colour them in. Fix them to a stick.

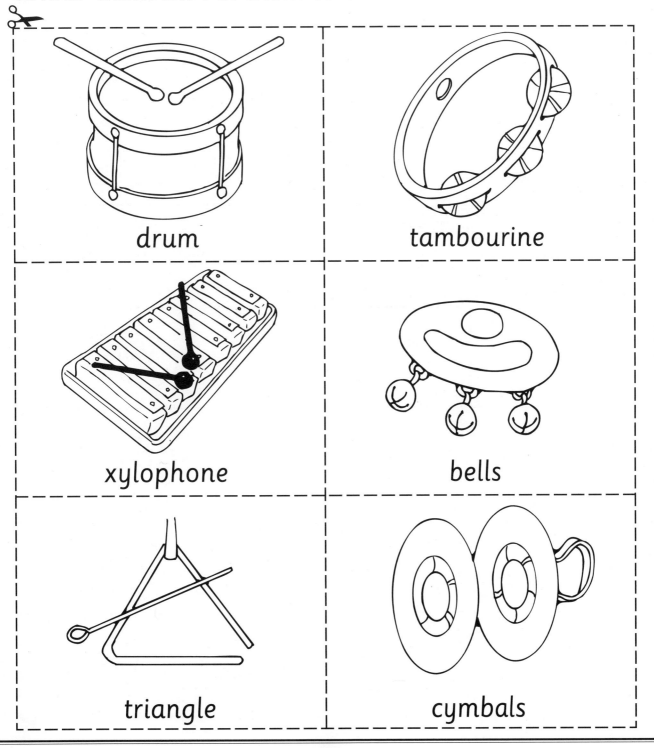

drum	tambourine
xylophone	bells
triangle	cymbals

Stairways

Colour in the stairs.

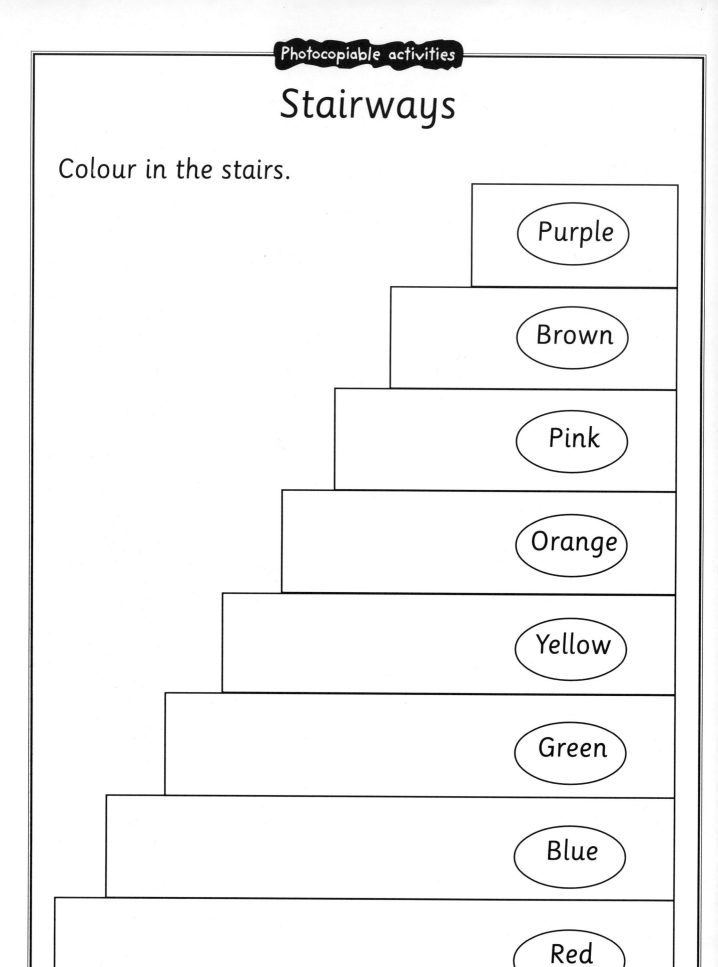

Musical maps

Make your own tune! Colour in the symbols. Cut them out and stick them on a square. Play the music.

START

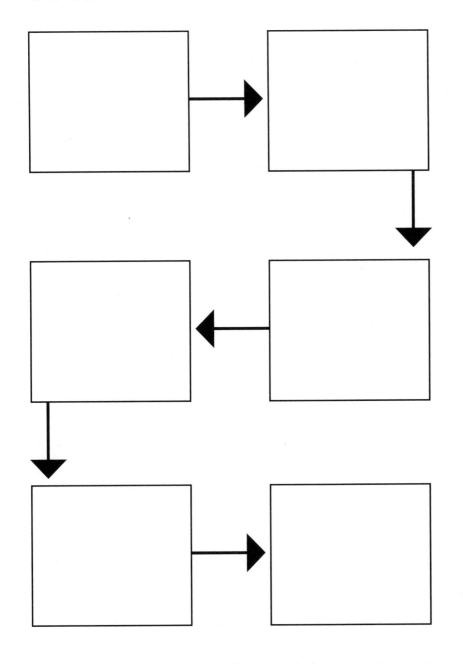

bells

drum

triangle

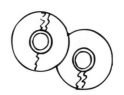

cymbals

bells

shakers

Learning in the Early Years - Photocopiable Activities
Creative Development

Notation grids

Draw in some beats or shakes for each instrument.
Play your music.

drum	
triangle	
cymbals	
bells	
shakers	

Louder, softer

Colour in and cut out the cards.

Picture beats

Colour in the pictures. Cut out the cards.

chair

table

television

teddy

ball

telephone

flower

computer

box

chapter two

Art

Mix colours, match shades and develop decoration skills with the varied and interesting ideas in this chapter. Ideas include using everyday materials such as pasta and seeds to make interesting textures and using wax crayons to develop wax resist pictures.

Colour magic
Learning objective
To learn about colour mixing.
What to do
Enlarge the sheet to A3 and provide one for each child. Have blue, red and yellow paint and mixing palettes ready. Let the children match and paint in the first blob on the sheet, then the second. Encourage them to mix the two colours together and paint in the final blob. Repeat this for the whole sheet.

Talk about all the things they know which are the same colours. Cut out small coloured pictures from catalogues and stick them by the correct colour.

Fantasy flowers
Learning objective
To make a collage.
What to do
Give each child a copy of the sheet and ask them to colour the shapes as leaves or petals or leave them white. Look at different flowers and talk about how petals make up flowers. Ask the children to cut out the shapes they have coloured and build up a three-dimensional form of a flower on plain paper by applying glue to an edge of the shape and bending the remainder upwards. When they are dry, cut them out, add a paper stalk and display them in a basket or flat on a board.

Matching colours
Learning objective
To mix different shades of colour.
What you do
This can be undertaken at different times of the year but is very effective in spring or autumn when the colours of leaves are particularly interesting.

Working with a group of six or seven children, gather a selection of leaves and give each child a sheet. Ask them to sort the leaves by size and select four to fit the boxes on their sheets. Stick them down with glue. Have an appropriate range of paints ready and demonstrate how to mix different colours and shades. Let the children mix matching colours to paint in the boxes beside their leaves.

Magic boxes

Learning objective
To design and make a box
What you do
Work with just three or four children for this activity. Photocopy or stick a sheet onto card for each child. Talk about what tiny things they could keep in a 'magic box'. Ask the children to draw their ideas on the box shape, using felt-tipped pens. Next, help them to cut out the shape and fold along the dotted lines and flaps. Glue the flaps, holding them together with paper clips until they are dry. Let the children decorate the outside of the boxes with beads and shiny materials and suspend them from a corner of the room to twist and catch the light.

Cut wool creatures

Learning objective
To create a textile animal.
What you do
Enlarge the sheet to A3 for each child. Have threads and woven fabrics available in suitable colours to decorate the animals. Show the children pictures of the animals shown on the sheet in information books and talk about their colourings and the textures of their

coats. Help them select suitable fabrics and pull the threads out of the weave, cutting them into 1cm lengths. Next, put thick glue over their chosen animal and stick the chopped threads to create a furry creature. When dry, cut out the animals and display them. Talk about suitable habitats for each creature and display them among twigs or leaves.

Texture blocks

PAGE 22

Learning objective
To experiment with textures.

What you do
Have containers of sand, non-poisonous seeds, small pasta shapes, pieces of foil and fabrics ready. Give each child a copy of the sheet. Talk about everyday objects and their textures.

Let the children spread glue thickly on each shape on the sheet and sprinkle on either sand, seeds or one of the other materials available. Repeat choosing different textures. When the shapes are dry, cut them out and let the children display them, deciding which are 'rough' and which are 'smooth'.

Wax resist

PAGE 23

Learning objective
To make a water resistant effect picture.

What you do
Enlarge the photocopiable sheet and give one copy to each child. Ask the children to colour in the space shapes using pale coloured wax crayons. Tell them to press heavily. Next, encourage them to paint a thin layer of black paint over the entire sheet. The shapes covered in crayon will be revealed! Talk about how the paint cannot reach the paper because the wax 'resists' the water and forms a barrier.

Blazing butterflies

PAGE 24

Learning objective
To design hanging 3D butterflies.

What you do
Photocopy or stick the sheets onto card, and give one copy to each child. Show the children pictures of different butterflies in books and talk about the patterns and symmetry. Let the children cut out the butterfly shape and help them to fold it along the centre of the body. Ask them to paint one side of the butterfly shape, fold it over and press down firmly to create a symmetrical pattern. When dry, turn the shape over and repeat on the reverse side. Attach threads and suspend the butterflies from strings across the room.

Fluttering flags

PAGE 25

Learning objective
To make flag designs.

What you do
Talk about the different designs shown on the sheet. Trace over the main sections of flag and cut them out. Help the children to use these as patterns to pin and cut out shapes in different fabrics. Glue them in place. Add other scraps to make different designs. Roll the top of the sheet around a small stick and fasten firmly. Hang the flags like bunting around your room.

Toe the line!

PAGE 26

Learning objective
To explore line in drawing.

What you do
Give each child a copy of the sheet and a thick pencil. Talk about the different marks in the boxes and show the children how to make them. Ask the children to fill each box to match the marks shown.

Colour magic

Paint in the splodges and mix a new colour.

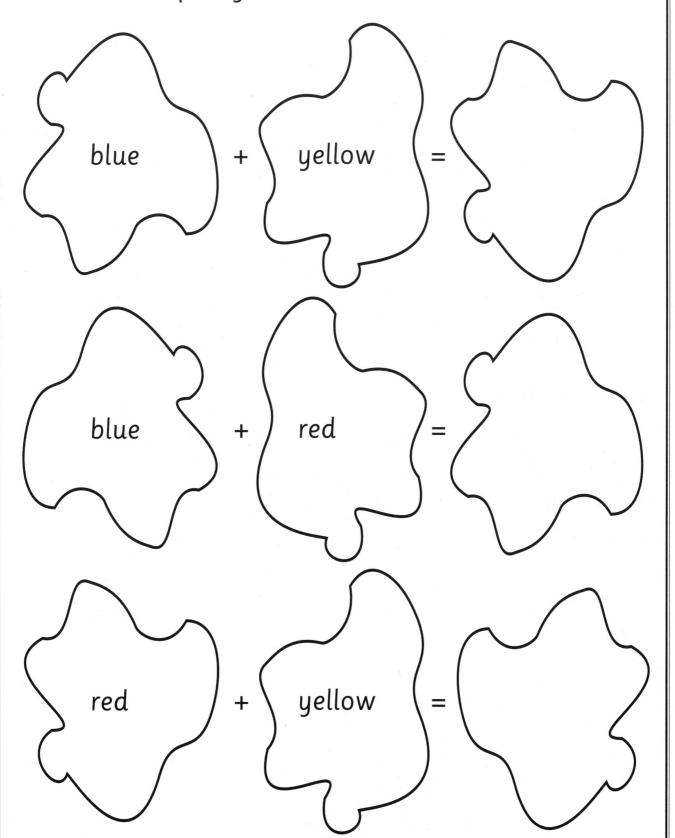

blue + yellow =

blue + red =

red + yellow =

Fantasy flowers

Colour and cut the petals to make collage flowers.

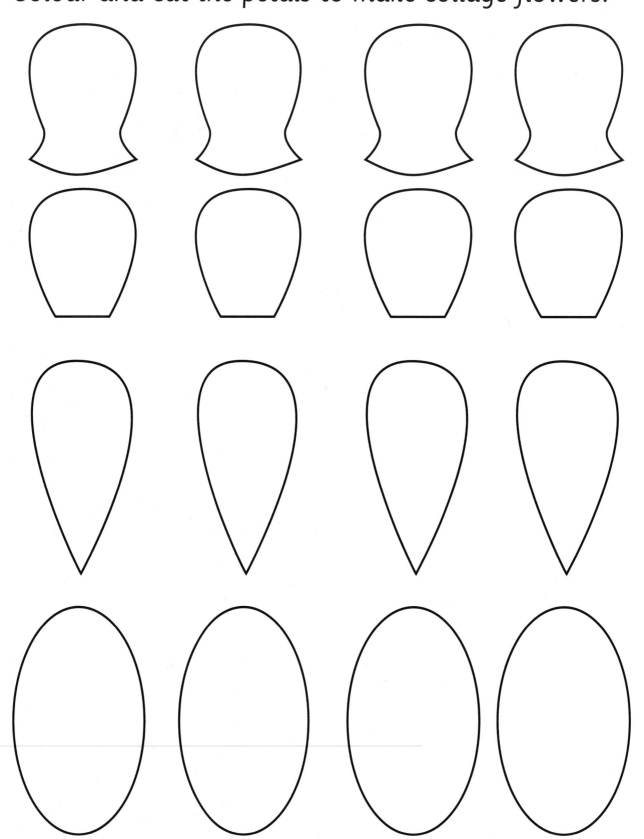

Matching colours

Stick some leaves here. Can you mix different colours to match them?

Leaves	Matching colours

Magic boxes

Colour in some patterns, fold along the dotted lines and make a box.

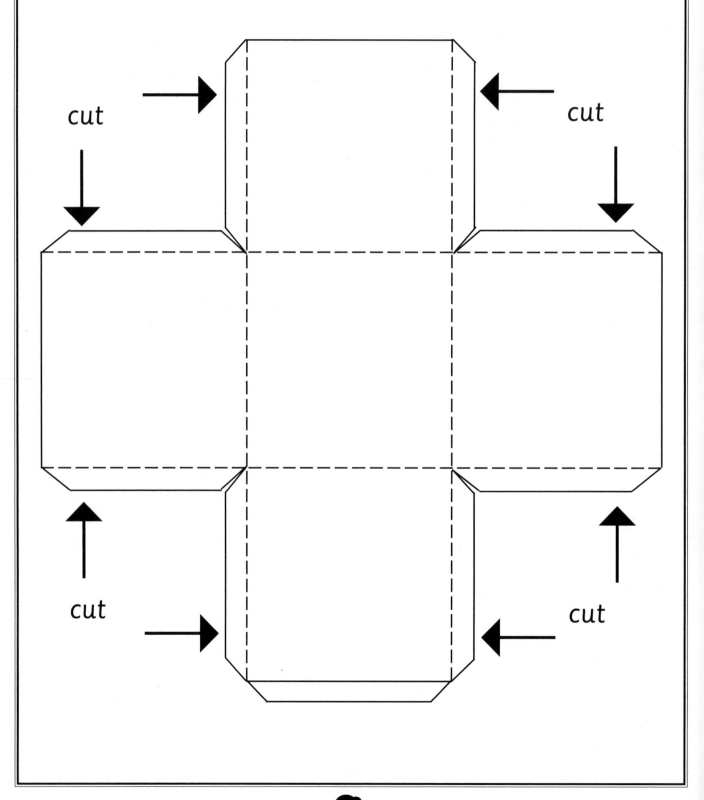

cut

cut

cut

cut

Cut wool creatures

Decorate the animals and cut them out.

Cat

Owl

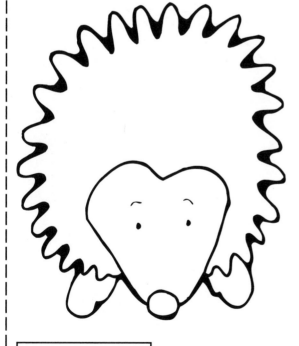

Hedgehog

Rabbit

Texture blocks

Cover each shape with glue and decorate.

Square

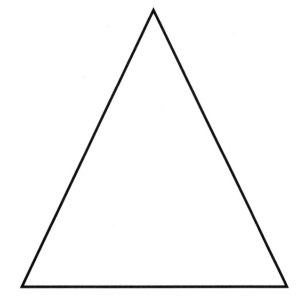

Triangle

Heart

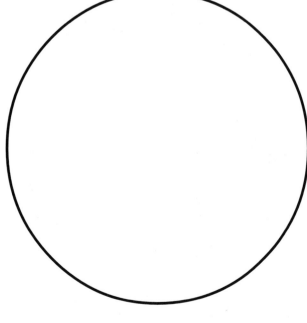

Circle

Wax resist

Colour in the shapes with pale wax crayons then paint the whole sheet with dark paint. Watch your shapes appear!

Blazing butterflies

Cut out the butterfly and fold along the line.

Paint the butterfly on the front and back.

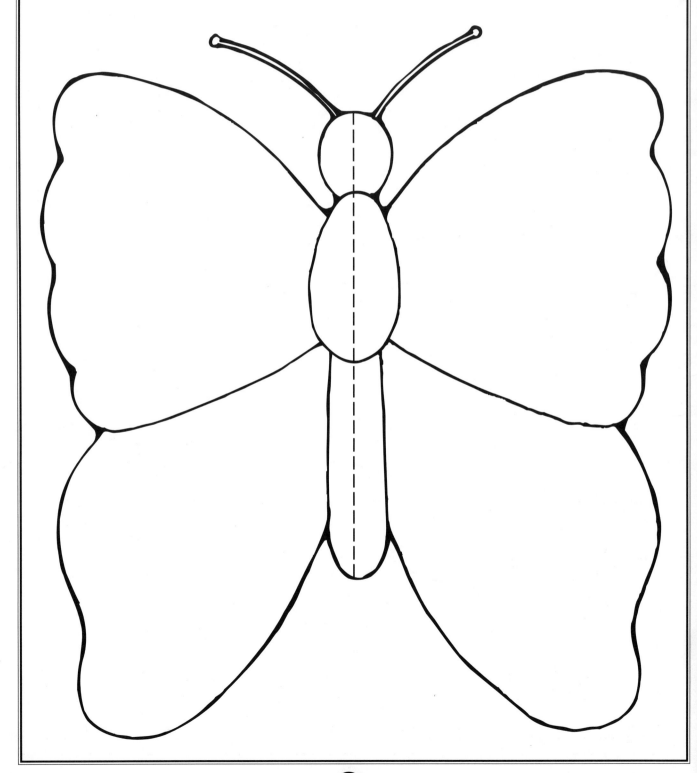

Fluttering flags

Use these shapes to make patterns for a flag.

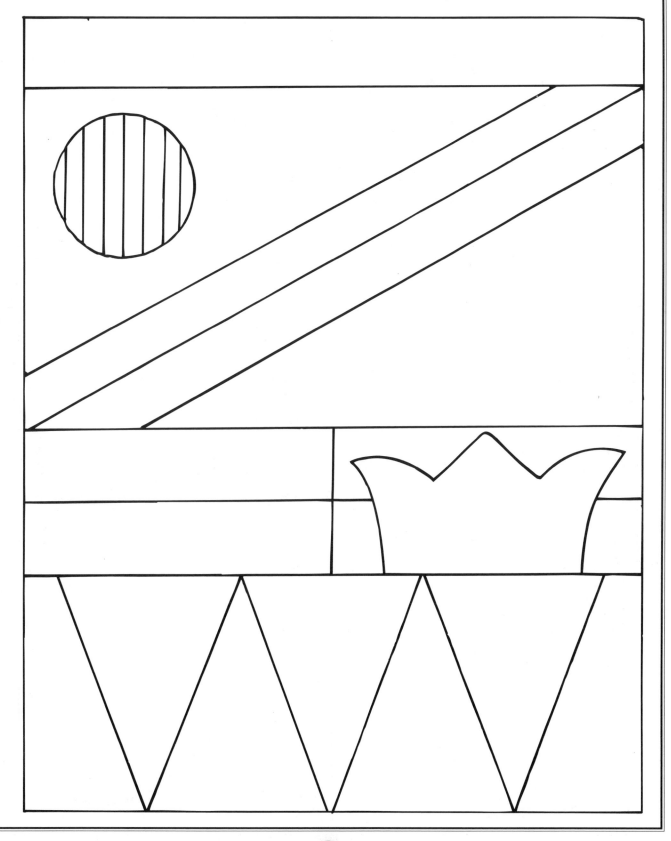

Learning in the Early Years - Photocopiable Activities
Creative Development

Toe the line!

Can you copy these marks and fill the whole box?

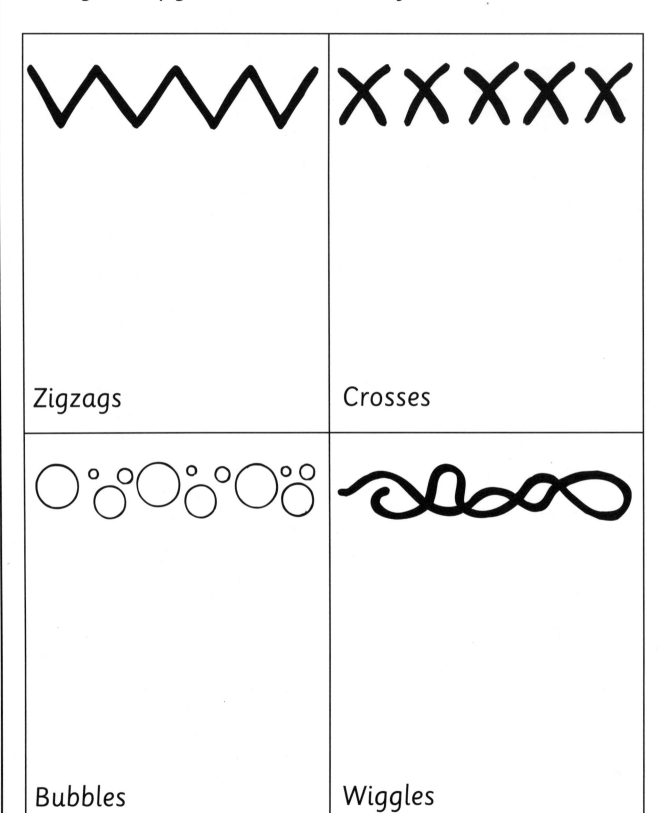

Zigzags

Crosses

Bubbles

Wiggles

chapter three

Craft

Develop your children's skills with this range of activities which include opportunities for weaving, sewing, mask making and collage work. Encourage creative input by providing a wide range of materials and colours for the children to work with.

PAGE 29

Weaving strips
Learning objective
To learn a simple weaving technique.
What you do
Copy the sheet and give one to each child. Ask them to cut very carefully along the lines stopping at the large dots. Cut strips of different coloured papers (sugar, wrapping, newspaper and so on) each about 2cm wide and 30cm long. Show the children how to weave these strips, pushing the cut strips under and over the coloured paper. Let them choose different papers and help them to weave each row, leaving about 4cm overlap at each end. Talk about the under-over process and the patterns that emerge. When completed, fold the overlaps underneath and tape them down firmly. Use the finished sheets as snack-time placemats.

PAGE 30

Flower power
Learning objective
To learn a simple sewing technique.
What you do
Photocopy or stick the sheet onto card and use a thick needle to make the holes as indicated. Give a sheet to each child. Have available a selection of bright threads, scissors and large-eyed needles (with rounded ends for safety). Let the children select colours and help them to thread their needles, doubling the thread with a large knot at the end. Show them how to sew up and down through the rows of holes. Let them sew around the outer row, helping them to fasten off and thread new colours. Let them weave in and out of their stitches. Talk about the process they are using and the effects they are creating. When completed, cut round the flowers and display them together.

PAGE 31

Venetian masks
Learning objective
To make a Venetian-style mask.
What you do
Work in small groups. Give each child a sheet that has been firmly stuck, or photocopied, onto card and ask them to cut out the shape. Help them by cutting out the eye-holes. Tell the children about masked balls in Venice and how people wear elaborate masks to hide their identities – until midnight when everyone removes them! Have a collection of feathers and sequins (available from art shops and haberdashers) and encourage the children to cover their masks completely so that no card is showing. When dry, thread elastic through the sides and let the children wear them to dance or use them for dressing up.

PAGE 32

Making beads
Learning objective
To make paper beads and jewellery.
What you do
Make some paper beads before the session and show these to the children, explaining that they are going to make some jewellery. Talk about different necklaces, bracelets, brooches and earrings. Give each child a copy of the sheet and ask them to colour the triangles in strong colours (paint, felt-tipped pens or crayons). When the sheets are dry, cut them out and apply glue to the plain side. Help the children roll them over an old pencil, starting with the widest side and rolling towards the tip. Slide them carefully off the pencil and leave to dry. Encourage the children to thread the beads onto laces or string to make necklaces, bracelets and earrings (looped over their ears).

PAGE 33

3D trees
Learning objective
To make simple 3D constructions.
What you do
Work with a small group of three to four children at a time. Photocopy the sheet to provide two copies for each child. Make a collection of twigs, each around 30cm long, with the children. Fill tiny flowerpots with sand or soil and stick a twig in each. Talk about leaf shapes and how different trees have particular leaves. Let the children cut out the leaves and paint or colour both sides. Then let them choose and share out the shapes so that each child has a matching set. Help them fix the leaves to the twig 'branches' with a strong glue – balancing them on the twig until they dry. Put all the trees together to make a model wood or use them as part of a village, farm or small world play activities.

PAGE 34

Gift baskets
Learning objective
To construct 3D structures from paper.
What you do
This can be an ideal activity for Mother's Day, Easter, Eid or Christmas by choosing appropriate colours and contents to suit the particular festival. Photocopy or mount the sheet onto card and give one to each child. You will also need about 40cm of thin ribbon or bright wool for each basket plus 10cm for the handle. Talk about baskets, what they are used for and how they can be made of natural materials such as willow or man-made materials such as plastic. Ask the children to colour and cut out the shapes carefully. Use a hole punch to make the holes as indicated. Help them to thread the ribbon through the basket holes, pull it into shape and tie a bow. Repeat this for the handle. Fill the baskets with shredded tissue and a small gift to take home!

PAGE 35

Spinning delights
Learning objective
To make simple mobiles.
What you do
Photocopy or mount copies of the sheet onto card. You will need a thin wire coat hanger for each child, plus thread and a hole punch. Talk about the sea and the creatures on the sheet, showing pictures in information books if possible. Explain what a mobile is and how it looks. Ask the children to paint or colour in the creatures, then cut out the shapes and word cards. Punch holes as indicated and tie different lengths of thread to each item, suspending them along the hanger. Display the hangers along a washing line in your room.

Magic carpets
PAGE 36
Learning objective
To explore textiles and make patterns.
What you do
Tell the children the story of Ali Baba and magic carpets. Talk about carpets, what they are made of and the patterns and colours. Have a collection of fabric scraps and trimmings, including a fringing or a suitable edging available. Give each child a copy of the sheet and talk about the carpet shape and design. Ask them to choose and glue on strips of fabric to cover the carpet, adding other shapes to make interesting patterns and finishing with a suitable carpet fringe or edging. With younger children you may prefer to pre-cut a range of strips and shapes. Display the carpets and help the children write a label saying where their magic carpet took them.

Weaving strips

Cut along the lines and weave paper strips in and out.

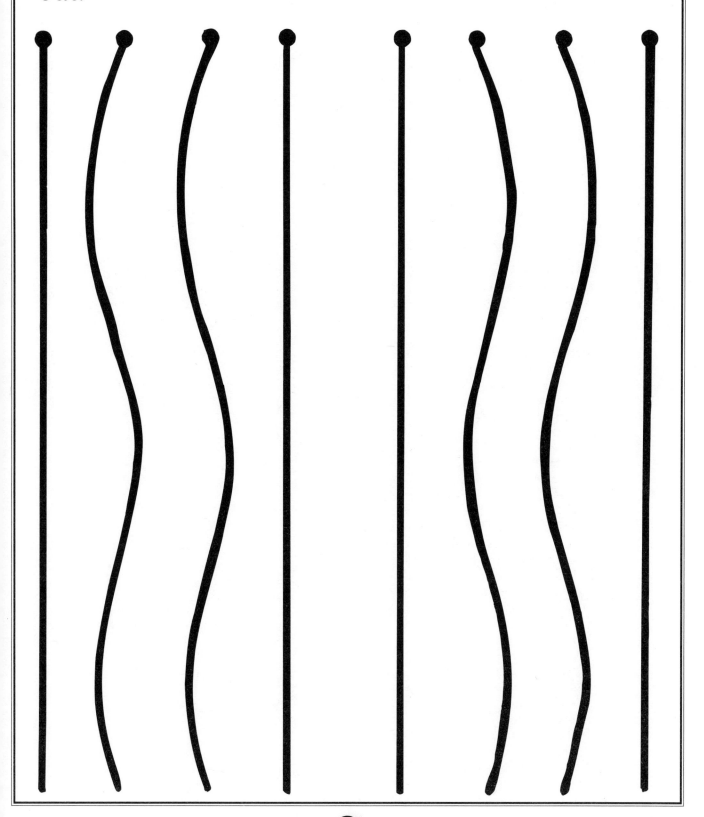

Flower power

Sew thread through the dots.

Venetian masks

Can you decorate your mask using feathers, glitter and trimmings?

Making beads

Colour these shapes and cut them out. Glue the back and roll round a pencil, base to tip.

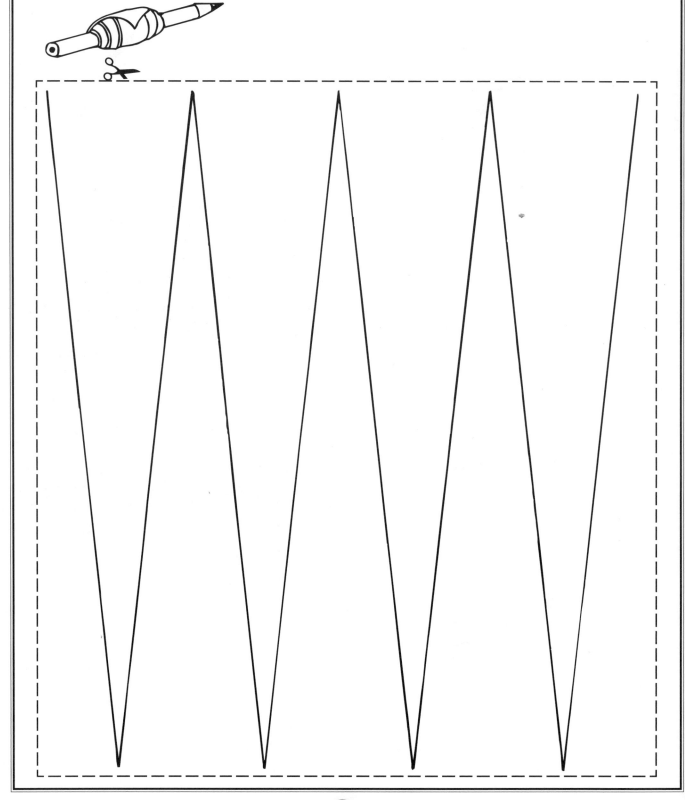

Learning in the Early Years - Photocopiable Activities
Creative Development

3D trees

Colour, cut out and stick these leaves to some twigs.

Gift baskets

Make a basket to carry something special.

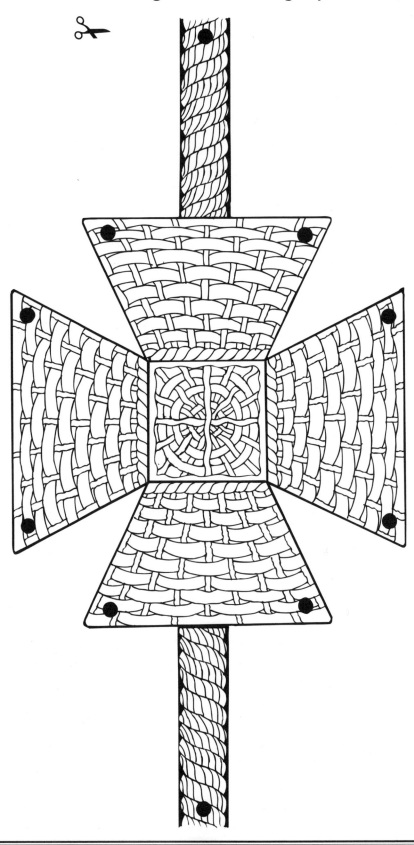

Spinning delights

Colour in these underwater creatures and make a mobile.

Dolphin

Starfish

Shell

Fish

Magic carpets

Can you make a special magic carpet?

Stick on some fabric and trimmings to create your own carpet pattern.

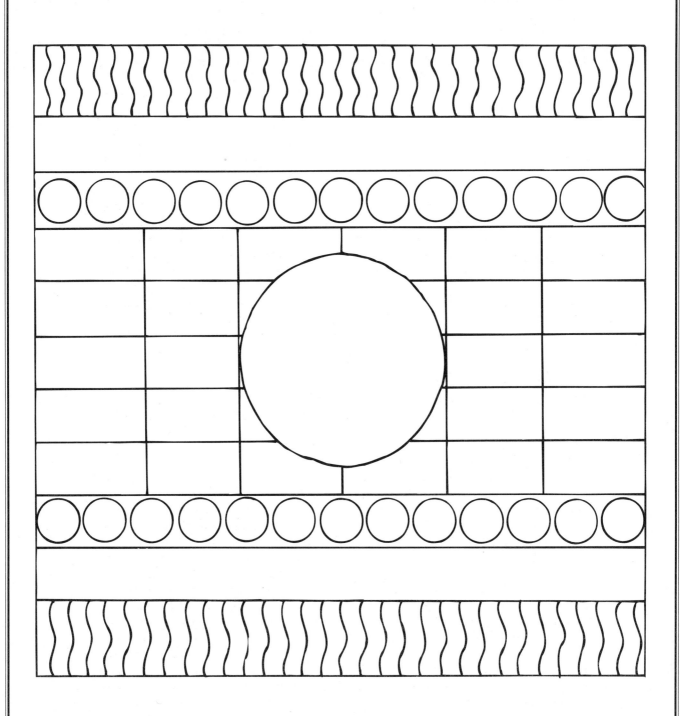

chapter four

Drama and dance

Use your children's natural enthusiasm for dance and drama with this selection of ideas to develop their skills, including making characters and props for use in simple plays. Ideas also include learning about shadow puppets, making up stories and using finger puppets.

PAGE 40

Glove puppets
Learning objective
To make puppet characters.
What to do
Talk to the children about glove puppets and show them one you have made, pointing out the features. Working with groups of two to three children at a time, ask them to choose an animal or character for their puppet. Give each child a sheet and ask them to cut round the puppet shape very carefully. Help them pin the paper pattern to two thicknesses of felt and cut out the shapes. Help the children to spread glue around the edges and press the two pieces together leaving an opening at the bottom. Help them to cut out features including eyes, nose and ears from the felt scraps and stick them to the puppet. Leave the puppets to dry. Let the children make up plays and perform them to each other.

PAGE 41

Colourful characters
Learning objective
To make and use box theatre puppets.
What to do
Make up some puppets of your own, using the photocopiable page, to show the children. Explain how children in the past made their own puppet theatres and could buy coloured printed sheets for two old pennies. Copy or stick copies of the sheet onto card and give one to each child. Talk about the characters on the sheet, what they look like and who they might be. Ask the children to colour the people in carefully using brightly coloured crayons or felt-tipped pens. Help them cut out the characters and tape them to thin sticks.

Show the children how to slide their puppets along the table and let them perform fairy stories to each other.

PAGE 42

Shoe box theatre
Learning objective
To make and use theatre scenery
What to do
You will need a shoe box, or similar, sheets of wallpaper and a copy of the sheet for each child. Cut side sections out of the boxes as shown on the sheet. Pre-cut pieces of wallpaper to fit the base of the box. Prepare a finished 'theatre' to show the children and, if you have made the puppets in Colourful characters (page 41), have these ready. Talk about Victorian puppet theatres and show the children how the puppets are in a house scene. Let them each choose a sheet of wallpaper and glue it to the back wall of their scene. Next, ask them to colour in the scenery. Cut out the shapes and help the children glue them in place within the house. Use the character puppets to act out simple scenes.

PAGE 43

Castle scenes
Learning objective
To learn about changing scenery in the theatre.
What to do
Use the shoe box theatres from the activity on page 42. Cut sheets of card to fit the base and act as a change of scenery for each child. Talk about the theatre and how the scenery can be changed. Read the story of 'Sleeping Beauty' to the children.

Give each child a copy of the sheet and let them cut out and colour the scenery. Let them arrange and stick the scenery onto the card, drawing in other features such as sky, thorn hedges, trees and so on. Make sliding puppets (as in Colourful characters on page 41) using the children's own drawn figures.

37

Underwater scene

PAGE 44

Learning objective

To extend imaginative ideas in drama.

What to do

Talk about things that are under the sea. Read *The Rainbow Fish* by Martin Pfister(North-South Books) or similar stories. Explain that in drama we can pretend to be anywhere we want, even in places we couldn't really live, such as under the sea. Give each child a copy of the sheet and talk about the things on it. Then proceed as for 'Shoe box theatre' and 'Castle scenes', making the scenery. Encourage the children to make fish or mermaid figures to use with this scenery.

Storyboards

PAGE 45

Learning objective

To make up imaginative stories.

What to do

Enlarge a copy of the sheet for each child plus one for yourself. Read a favourite story to the children, stopping frequently to ask *What happened first? What happened next? What happened in the end?* Use your storyboard to demonstrate. Remind them of the first stage of the story and make a quick pin man sketch in the first box. Act as scribe to write a simple sentence dictated by the children underneath. Repeat for the middle and last boxes. Explain that film and TV writers use 'storyboards' like these to work out how they will set up each scene. Give each child a copy of the sheet and ask them to draw pictures of the beginning, middle and end of the story. Act as scribe to record their ideas. Make a 'Storyboard' book to share.

Shadow puppets

PAGE 46

Learning objective

To learn about shadow puppets.

What to do

Work with small groups of two to three children at a time. You will need two short sticks, paper fasteners, sticky tape and a sheet for each child, glued to black paper, plus a box theatre set up as shown on the sheet.

Use a torch and the 'theatre' to show the children how shadows are made. Encourage the children to cut out the figures carefully. Push paper fasteners through the marks to make a moving arm. Help the children to tape one stick to the body and the other to the hand, fastening it to the white side. Let them hold the body stick still and gently move the arm stick to make a movement. Take turns in the theatre and let the other children suggest things for the puppets to say and do.

Secret treasures!

PAGE 47

Learning objective

To stimulate imaginative responses.

What to do

Work with five or six children at a time. Enlarge a sheet for each child. Cut out and fold each sheet as shown with the 'secret' section marked on the back.

Have a collection of catalogues, cards and pictures ready. Talk about favourite things that are special to us. Show the children a blank book with a 'secret place'. Tell them that they can choose pictures of their favourite things to hide in the middle. Open up the sheets to the secret section. Let the children choose pictures, cut them out and stick them in. When dry, refold the books. Read each child's book together as they turn the pages, revealing their secrets and talking about their choices. Display the books on a table so the secrets are on show!

Finger figures

PAGE 48

Learning objective

To make and use finger puppets.

What to do

Photocopy or stick a copy of the sheet onto thin card for each child. Let the children cut out the shapes, helping them by cutting out the finger holes. Push your fingers through a card shape to demonstrate how the 'legs' work. Talk about different characters in stories and explain that the children are going to make finger figures linked with characters in a story that you have read together recently.

Ask the children to select from fabric scraps, wool, beads and trimmings and stick them onto the shapes to create characters. When they are finished, let the children make them 'walk' and ask them to invent a story – or act one out as you retell a tale.

Streamers

PAGE 49

Learning objective

To extend whole-arm dance movements.

What to do

Work with a group of five to six children at a time. You will need felt-tipped pens, glue, glitter, small sticks, scissors and clear sticky-backed plastic. Photocopy or stick copies of the sheet onto card, one for each child. Ask them to colour in the spiral shape in bright colours. Add dabs of glue along the swirly shape and sprinkle with glitter. When dry, carefully cover with plastic sheet on both sides. Help the children cut along the spiral lines. Tape the end firmly to a stick.

Ask the children to hold the sticks and make large arm movements, watching the patterns their streamers make. Ask them to imitate your movements – up and down, round and round, slow, fast, high and low. Play different types of music and ask the children to make appropriate movements.

Directions

PAGE 50

Learning objective

To explore left and right dance directions.

What to do

Work with groups of five to six children at a time. You will need thin elastic, sticky tape and a sheet (copied or glued onto card) for each child. Make yourself a set in advance. Show the children how they can tell their left hand from their right by asking them to hold out their hands with their thumbs extended at right angles. The fingers/thumb on the left hand will make an 'L' shape.

Ask the children to paint or colour the mitts using red for left and green for right (matching red for port and green for starboard) and cut them out. Put a small piece of sticky tape over the marked holes to prevent tearing and use a punch to make the holes. Tie elastic across to keep the mitt in place, and help the children to put on their mitts correctly. Remind them of the colours and ask them to wave their left and right hands alternately. Use your mitts and ask them to copy your arm movements. Let the children take turns to lead movements for the others to copy. Next, ask them to put out their right hands and move to the right. Repeat to the left. Vary the speed and ways of moving.

Nifty movers

PAGE 51

Learning objective

To learn to move in different ways.

What to do

Photocopy or stick copies of the sheet onto card, one for each child. Talk about the animals on the sheet and how they move. Ask the children to colour the pictures and cut them out. Thread string through the holes to form a necklace. Let the children choose which card to wear and ask them to move in the correct way. Let them observe each other, repeating the activity. Play Saint-Saëns' 'Carnival of the Animals' and let the children choose and wear a 'necklace' and move appropriately. Repeat, then let them draw other animals on the back and invent new movements.

Pathways

PAGE 52

Learning objective

To learn a personal sequence movement.

What to do

Work with groups of eight children at a time. Photocopy or stick the sheets onto thin card, one for each child. Ask them to colour the arrows brightly, then cut them out carefully. Make yourself a set too. Let the children find a space and practise jumping, hopping, walking and running forwards, backwards and sideways in the space. Demonstrate and talk about different movement directions, laying the arrows down in order. Repeat to show that you are following the arrows to make a pattern.

Let the children put their arrows down and ask them to follow their patterns. Encourage older children to put them in correct numerical order. Let them watch each other. Follow a child's pattern and encourage them to say if it's right. Next, use a tambourine or similar instrument and, varying the speed you play it, ask the children to follow their arrow pathway to your beat. Repeat. Finally, make a long twisting line of all the arrows and play 'Follow my leader'!

Glove puppets

Cut out these shapes to make your own puppet.

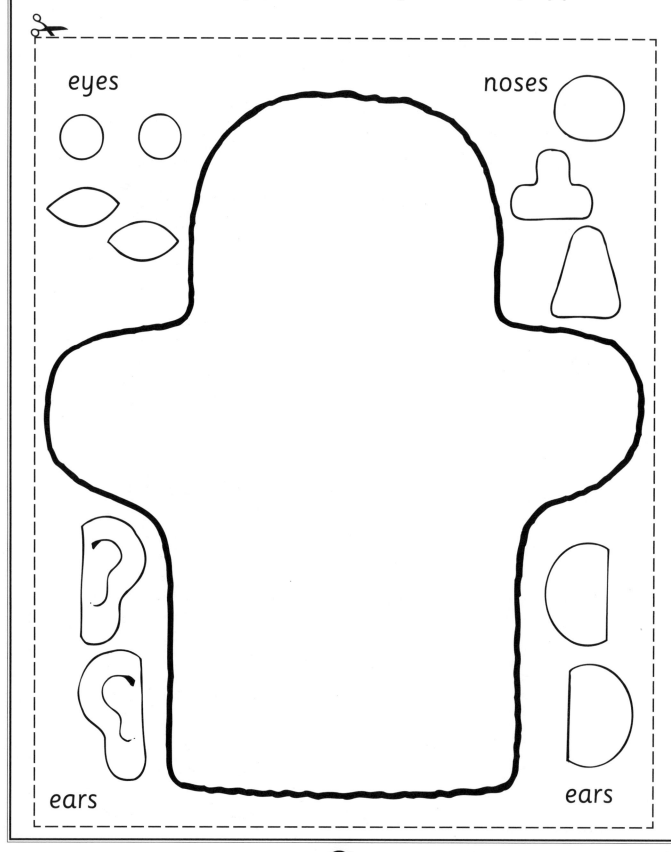

eyes

noses

ears

ears

Colourful characters

Colour these in to make some characters for a play.

41

Shoe box theatre

Use these to make a scene in your shoe box.

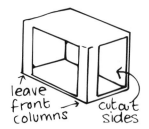

leave
front
columns

cut out
sides

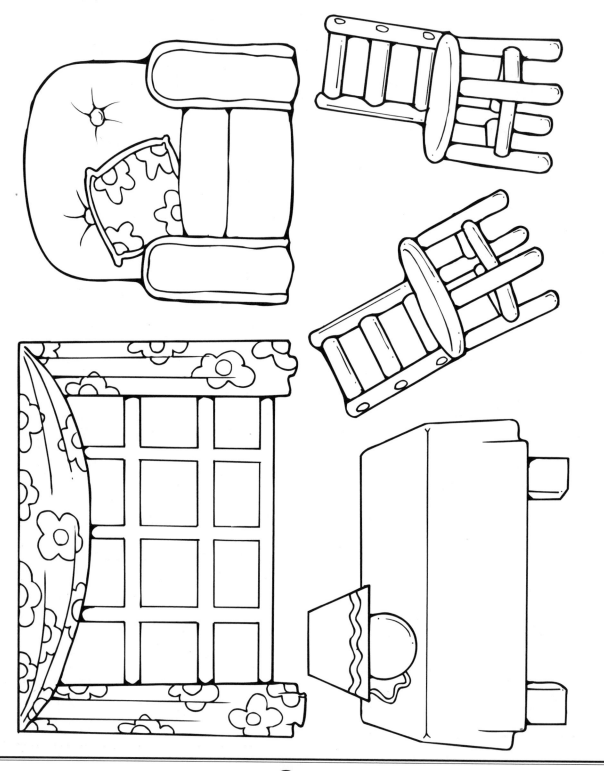

Castle scenes

Cut these out to make a castle in your shoe box.

43

Underwater scene

Colour, cut out and use as scenery.

Storyboards

What happens in your story? Draw the sequence here.

In the beginning...

Next...

In the end...

Shadow puppets

Cut out these shapes and fasten the arms on.

sticky tape

torch

cloth

box

Learning in the Early Years - Photocopiable Activities
Creative Development

Secret treasures!

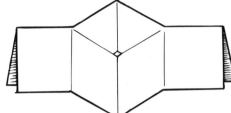

Fold as shown.

Draw and glue the treasure on the reverse side.

Here is my secret treasure!

Look inside!

CUT

No!

My secret treasure

Is it here?

Finger figures

Make some characters for your story.

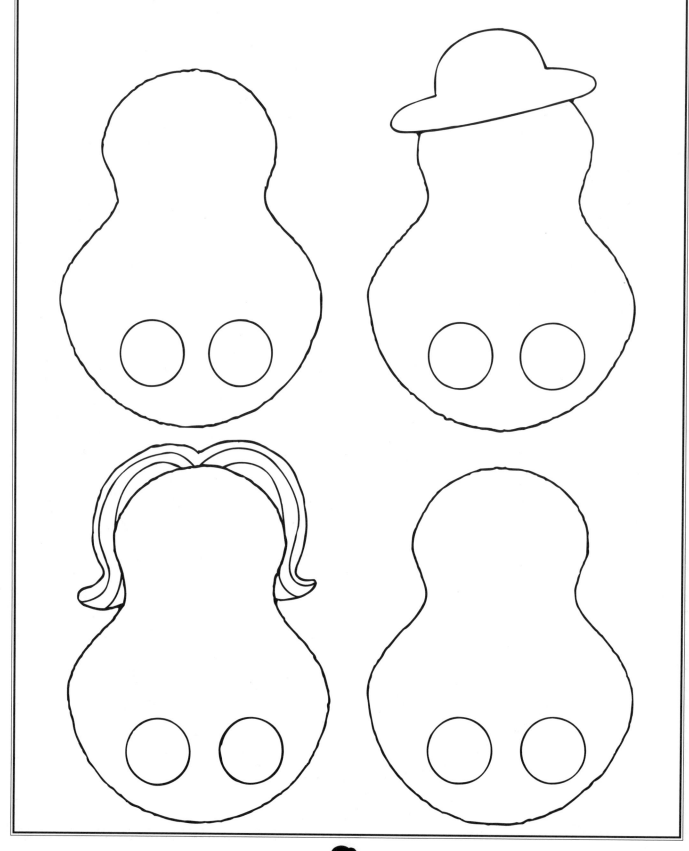

Streamers

Decorate with bright colours to make a streamer.

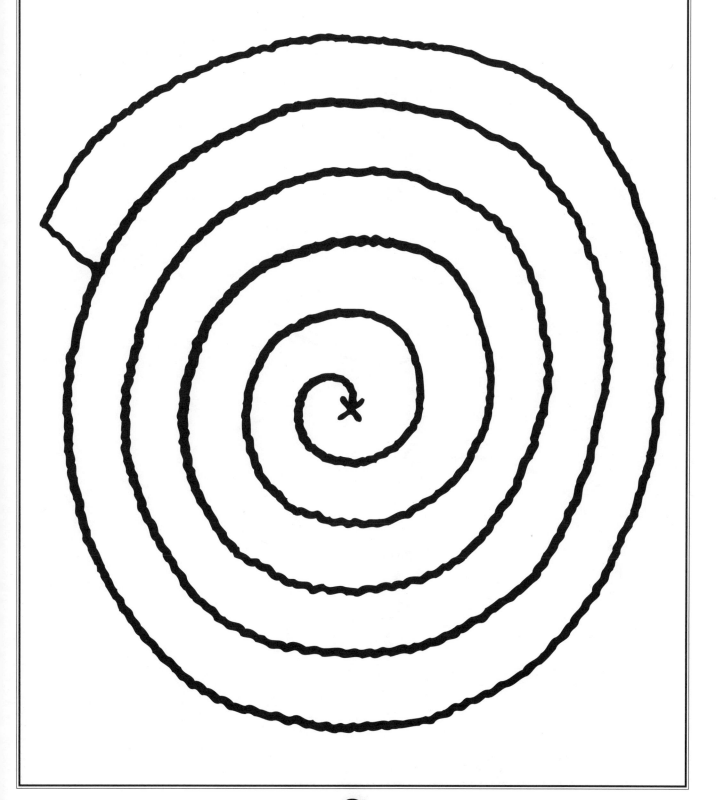

Learning in the Early Years - Photocopiable Activities
Creative Development

Directions

Make some mittens to tell your left from your right.

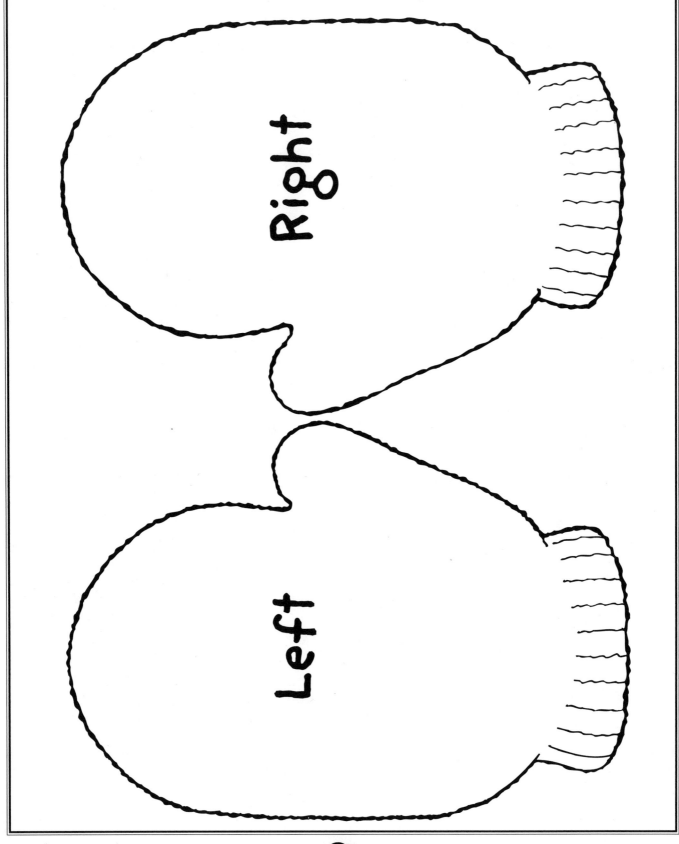

Nifty movers

I'm moving like a

I'm moving like an

I'm moving like a

I'm moving like a

Learning in the Early Years - Photocopiable Activities
Creative Development

Pathways

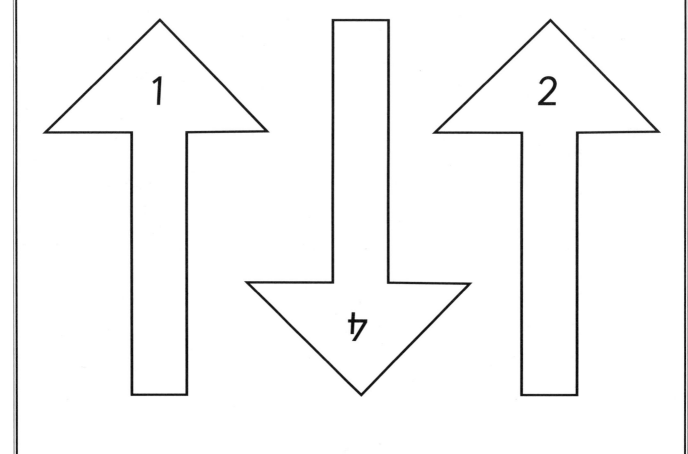

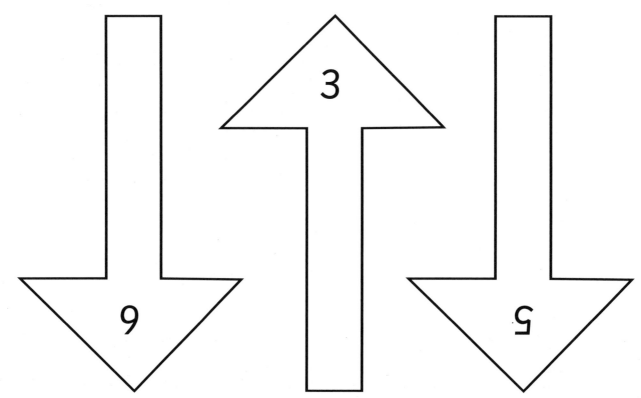

Learning in the Early Years - Photocopiable Activities
Creative Development

chapter five

Imaginative play

Focus role play on some specific themes such as a travel agents, a hospital, a garage and a restaurant with these ideas. Let the ideas develop as far as the children want to take them!

PAGE 55

Frolicking fish
Learning objective
To create and imagine an underwater environment.
What to do
Enlarge the sheet to A3 and mount or copy it onto card. Work in small groups and give two sheets to each child. Talk about different types of fish and ask them to cut out the shapes on the sheet. Ask them to match up the pairs and staple them together, stuffing them with scraps of paper. Paint, colour and glue on sequin scales then suspend the fish with lengths of green paper seaweed. Let the children pretend to be underwater explorers. You can also fasten fish to short sticks for the children to use as puppets.

PAGE 56

Travel agent
Learning objective
To role play a travel agency.
What to do
Work in small groups. Photocopy a sheet for each child. Talk about different holidays and ways of travelling. Set up an area to look like a travel agency with a desk, chairs, phone, 'computer', maps and brochures. Show the children a real passport and talk about when we need one. Ask them to cut out the passport and fold it in half. Help each child to fill in their passports neatly, drawing a 'photograph' of themselves and places they would like to visit on the inside pages.

PAGE 57

Hospitals
Learning objective
To learn about hospitals through play.
What to do
Work in a small group and have a sheet for each child. Have pictures of hospitals, nurses and patients available. Talk about treatment, charts and prescriptions, showing examples if possible. Ask the children to cut out the different sections of the sheet and show them how to fill in the forms, putting up an example for them to copy. Make a pad to use later by stapling all the prescriptions together. Set up an area with bed, table, chair and play medical equipment. Encourage the children to use them to role play, using the props from 'Hospital 'props' on page 58.

Hospital 'props'
PAGE 58
Learning objective
To learn about hospitals through play.
What to do
This small group activity would be usefully combined with 'Hospitals' on page 57. Glue a sheet onto card for each child. Let the children refer to pictures of nurses and doctors and hospital work. Ask the children to colour and fill in the name badges appropriately. Cut out the shapes and tape a large safety pin firmly to the back of each one. Let the children wear them to act out the roles of doctors and nurses, using toys as patients. Encourage positive discrimination with boys and girls playing doctors and nurses.

Animal masks
PAGE 59
Learning objective
To imagine being an animal.
What to do
Work in small groups. Enlarge the sheets so that the masks are large enough to fit the children's faces. Photocopy or stick the sheets onto thin card for each child. Provide pictures of

the animals for colour reference. Let the children colour in the animals and cut them out. Ask them to glue on feathers, fabric, wool and pipe-cleaners (for whiskers). Put sticky tape over the marked holes, punch a hole and thread elastic to secure them as masks. Let the children make up simple stories about the animal characters and act them out.

Garages
PAGE 60

Learning objective
To explore garages through role play.
What to do
Have a variety of adverts, pictures and model cars, together with examples of garage bills and an MOT certificate for this small group activity. Talk about the work done in garages and what registration numbers are. Give each child a sheet and ask them to cut out the bill and MOT certificate. Help them fill in the work docket. Set up an area with a table, toy tools, construction kits, toy cars and dressing-up clothes. Let the children use the dockets and MOT certificates in their play.

Bunting
PAGE 61

Learning objective
To create festive environments.
What to do
Work in groups of up to ten children. You will need some long lengths of tape and a stapler. The bunting can be used indoors, or outside if you cover each sheet with sticky-backed plastic after it has been decorated. Talk about occasions when people use decorations. Explain how bunting makes ordinary things attractive and festive. Set up an area for a shop or stall and ask the children to decorate it. Let them colour in the different flags brightly and stick on shiny scraps and beads. Cut them out and arrange them to spell 'fun' or in a chosen pattern. Staple the top edge to the tape and use to decorate the area.

Pairs of shoes
PAGE 62

Learning objective
To make 'stock' for a play shoe shop.
What to do
Working in small groups explain that the children are going to make shoes for a play shoe shop. Talk about different types of shoes, comparing their own with adverts. Have a collection of fabrics, buttons and trimmings available. Give each child a sheet and ask them to cut out the pairs of shoes, decorating them to match exactly. Glue each pair onto a long length of paper to make 'stock' on shelves or into a folder sugar paper 'catalogue'. Talk about costs and sizes and add price stickers. Count in twos! Use them to play shoe shops.

Menus
PAGE 63

Learning objective
To learn about restaurants through play.
What to do
Prepare an area to represent a café or restaurant with tables, chairs, crockery, cutlery, tablecloths, mats, flowers, candles and play food. Enlarge one sheet to be the café/restaurant wall list. Give one standard sheet, mounted on card, to each pair of children. Talk about cafés and restaurants, the different types of food they serve, who works there and who goes there to eat. Discuss favourite foods and let the children tell you what else to add to the menus, writing it on the large one for them to copy. Talk about and decide on prices. Let the children complete their menus taking turns to play at restaurateurs and customers.

Extraordinary villages
PAGE 64

Learning objective
To create imaginary houses.
What to do
Have a collection of junk materials available including clear plastics, foil, shiny materials, boxes, tubes, twigs and wooden off-cuts. Photocopy the sheet as large as possible for the children to work on in small groups. Explain that they are going to make amazing houses for the extraordinary village. Let them look at the map and help them to read the names of the different houses. Ask them to say what the different houses might be made from. Let them work in pairs to build a house from the scraps to fit onto the plan. Encourage them to talk about the imaginary families who live there and their adventures.

Frolicking fish

Make some shiny mobiles from these shapes.

Learning in the Early Years - Photocopiable Activities
Creative Development

T042755

Travel agent

Fill in your own notes.

Name

Age

Date of birth

Travelling to

Name

Passport

OFFICIAL STAMP OF APPROVAL

Hospitals

Nurse's Notes

Patient's name _____

Symptoms _____
_____
_____

Treatment _____
_____

Nurse's name _____
_____

City Hospital

Prescription form

Patient's name _____

Illness _____
_____

Medicine _____
_____

Instructions for use _____
_____
_____

Hospital 'props'

Animal masks

Make a cat or bird mask.

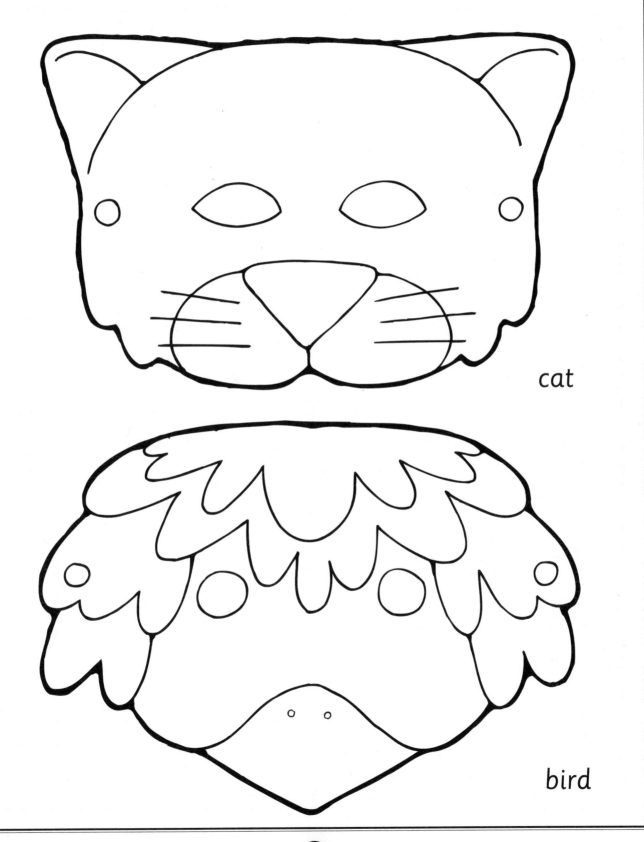

cat

bird

Learning in the Early Years - Photocopiable Activities
Creative Development

Garages

SpannerGarages Ltd

Name _____

Car _____

Number _____

Work to be done	Cost

Signed _____

Ministry of Transport Certificate

Car _____

Number _____

Passed/Failed its test _____

Tester's name _____

_____

Bunting

Colour, decorate and cut out the bunting.

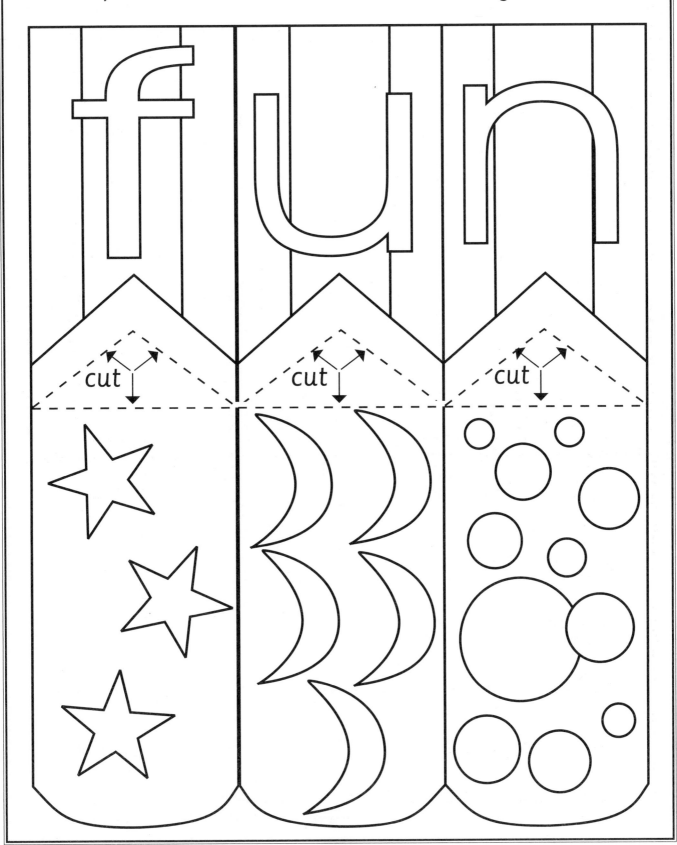

Name
_____

Pairs of shoes

Decorate the shoes to make matching pairs.

Learning in the Early Years - Photocopiable Activities
Creative Development

Menus

Fill in the menu and add prices.

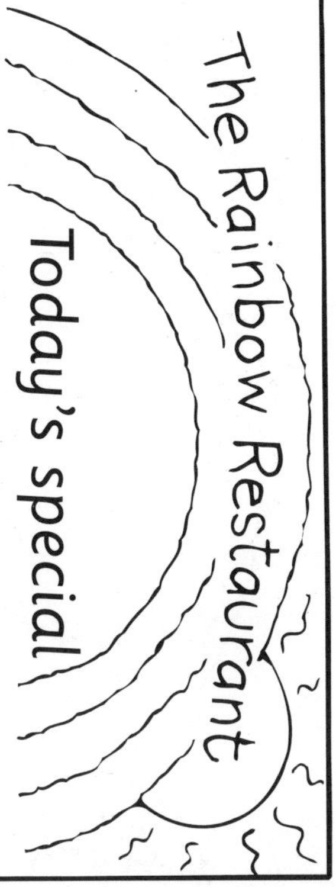

The Rainbow Restaurant

Today's special

Vegetable soup —————

••••••••••••

Fish and chips —————

Pizza —————

Samosas —————

Curry and rice —————

Noodles —————

Ice cream —————

Jelly —————

The Pop In Café

Tea —————

Coffee —————

Milk —————

Cakes —————

Biscuits —————

Sandwiches – egg —————

cheese —————

jam —————

tomato —————

Learning in the Early Years - Photocopiable Activities
Creative Development

Extraordinary villages

Colour in the map and make your own houses.